《走进新疆》丛书（第三辑）

主编：刘长明

THE MYSTERIOUS GREAT CANYON OF TIANSHAN MOUNTAIN

天山神秘大峡谷

THE VALLEY OF MAGIC

魔 幻 谷

于文胜 编著 by Yu Wensheng

新疆美术摄影出版社
新疆电子音像出版社

图书在版编目(CIP)数据

　　天山神秘大峡谷／于文胜著.—乌鲁木齐：新疆美术摄影
出版社：新疆电子音像出版社，2007.5
　　ISBN 7-80744-017-1

　　Ⅰ.天… Ⅱ.于… Ⅲ.①天山－峡谷－简介②民间故事－
作品集－中国 Ⅳ.P931.2　Ⅰ277.3

中国版本图书馆 CIP 数据核字（2006）第129471号

《走进新疆》丛书（第三辑）

主　编　刘长明

天山神秘大峡谷
魔幻谷

摄　　影　于文胜

撰　　文　梁彤谨　郁　笛

英文翻译　迪娜·迪里木拉提

责任编辑　文　昊

版式设计　党　红

封面设计　党　红

出　版　新疆美术摄影出版社
　　　　新疆电子音像出版社
　　　　（乌鲁木齐市西虹西路 36 号　830000）

发　行　新华书店

印　刷　海洋彩印有限公司

开　本　787mm×1092mm　1/24

印　张　5.5

字　数　12 千字　115 幅图片

版　次　2008 年 12 月第 2 版

印　次　2009 年 1 月第 1 次印刷

书　号　ISBN 7-80744-017-1

定　价　58.00 元

目　录

Content

THE MYSTERIOUS GREAT CANYON OF TIANSHAN MOUNTAIN

天山神秘大峡谷

天山神秘大峡谷位于阿克苏地区库车县北部72千米处217国道旁，呈东向西纵深长约5.5千米，为红褐色岩石经风雨雕刻而成。峡谷曲径通幽，别有洞天，山体千姿百态，峰峦直插云霄，沟中有沟，谷中有谷。南天门、幽灵谷、月牙峡、虎牙桥、魔天洞、雄师泪等景观造型生动，形态逼真。距谷口1.4千米处的山崖上有一处唐代石窟，窟内南、北、西壁上有残存壁画和汉文字。距峡谷700米处另有一峡谷，与神秘峡谷相伴。天山神秘大峡谷集雄、险、幽、静、神为一体，身临其境者无不赞美叫绝。

大峡谷近似呈南北弧形走向，开口处稍弯向东南，末端微向东北弯曲，由主谷和7条支谷组成，全长5000多米。谷端至谷口处自然落差200米以上，谷底最宽处53米，最窄处0.4米，仅容一人低头弯躯侧身通过。谷侧奇峰嶙峋，争相崛起；峰峦叠嶂，劈地擎天，崖奇石峭，磅礴神奇；神洞秘窟，各蕴其意。谷内蜿蜒曲折，峰回路转；步步有景，举目成趣；泉水叮咚，鸟叫蝉鸣，寒暑不浸，游人称绝。

整个峡谷犹如一条巨龙劈山而卧，呼风唤雨，神秘莫测。更令人称奇的是，距谷口1400米

The mysterious great Canyon of TianShan Mountain is located near national highway 217,about 72km from Kuche, Aksu. From east to east it's about 5.5km, it is formed of red and brown rock for thousands years. The canyon has various shape of mountains. Canyon contains more other valleys. The spot NANTIANMEN, YOULINGGU, YUEYAXIA, HUYAQIAO, MOTIANDONG, XIONGSHILEI are all vivid and verisimilar. A cliff about 1.4km from the mouth of canyon has a rock cave of Tang dynasty has mural and Chinese words on the south,north and west wall of the cave. There is another canyon beside the MAGIC VALLEY. The mysterious canyon of Tianshan Mountain is the most wonderful canyon which has many magic views.

The great canyon is arch shape and south to north direction, the mouth of it on the south-east, and tail on the north-east, it is formed with the main valley and seven branch valley, it has length of 5000m, the fall from mouth to tail is more than 200m, the widest on the bottom of valley is 53m, the narrowest place is only 0.4m, if you want to cross it ,you must

深处,高约 35 米的崖壁上,有一始建于盛唐时期壁画丹青的千佛洞遗址。就其文字记载和绘画艺术而言,在古西域地区至今已发现的 300 多座佛教石窟中绝无仅有,实属罕见。无山不成谷,峰奇谷更幽。峡谷区域平均海拔 1600 米,最高山峰 2048 米。组成峡谷的奇峰群山由赭色的泥质沙岩构成,当地维吾尔语叫做克孜利亚,即红色的山崖。

　　神秘大峡谷正处在当今我国 9 大影视基地之一的克孜利亚胜景中。庞大的红色山体群形成于距今 1.4 亿年前的中生代的白垩纪,经亿万年的风剥雨蚀,洪流冲刷,形成纵横交错,层叠有序的垄脊与沟槽,远看如诗如画,状若布达拉宫,仙天琼阁;近瞧若人似物,如梦似幻,惟妙惟肖,神韵万端,令人有鬼斧神工,奇景天成之慨叹。尤以谷口处的三座山体(奶头山、丽人山、佛面山)最为壮观。特别在夕阳斜射时,晚霞映山,极目远眺,天地间一片火红,令人大有不是火焰山,胜似火焰山之奇感。

head down,curb your body and sidle. The canyon will shock all the visitor who is in it with strange-shaped rock, spring and birds.

The entire valley is just like a mysterious dragon which drink the water of River of Kuche. More surprisingly is there is a Pak Ou Caves which is built in tang dynasty on 35m height and 1400m from the mouth of the valley. It is the only one in history of all the 300 caves in west region. The average elevation is 1600 in this area and the highest mountain is 2048m. The mountains of the Canyon are formed of ochreous mud nature sandstone, the local Uygur called them "Kzlia" which means "The Red Cliff"

The mysterious canyon is located in Kzlia scene which is one of the nine television base of china. The huge mountain was formed in the Cretaceous period from 14000000years ago. After so many years of rain and wind flush, it has many shapes and surprising points of view. Especially the three mountains on the mouth of the valley is more surprisingly. When the sun set, the mountain looks like on fire, it's greater than The Mountain Of Flames.

The blinding light and mysterious channel   炫目的光，神秘的甬道
Time was engrave on a long and narrow face   时光镌刻在一张狭长的脸上

4

是呀,让时间退却,这悬浮的宫殿
是一张多么干净的名片

Yep, to make time fall back
What a clear name card this suspended palace is

我们向上，仰望着天界
或者向下，在哪一个坠落的瞬间停下来

We look up to the universe
Or down sight and stop at the falling moment.

What makes me turn around and see the castle behind me
The whirl of loneliness never look back

是什么让我转过身去,看见身后的城堡
这寂寞的旋转,永不回头

这些被熄灭的火焰，自由的牙齿呀
我们咬不断时光的缠绕和千年的寂寞

These dead flame and free teeth
But we can not cut the convolve of time and
loneliness for thousands years

Some mountain was destined to be exceeded
And some lookout was destined the fact which has covered

有一些山峰注定会被超越
有一些眺望也注定了，被掩盖的事实

这是三个洞穴,三个巨人走失了
空留下这屋顶,神秘而空旷

Three giants lost and three caves left
Only the roof ,mysterious and hollowness

What stopped us to climb up
And what forces dig such a large window on the rock

是什么阻挡了，我们向上的攀援
是什么力量，凿开赤岩上的洞天

隐蔽在岩石后面的这一只犬呀
日出日落,守望神谷

The dog hidden behind the rock
Can never see the sun in such a deep cave

They said that this is a pair of dancing penguin

But where can you find a central glacier in this red valley

呵呵,他们说这是一对双舞的企鹅

可这赭红色的山谷里,哪里有一条世纪的冰川

Maybe you have entered the heaven of musing

How many years have you wait for this little rest

或者你已经进入了冥想的天界这一刻的小憩,已经等待了多少个轮回

Lookout at which direction
The non-changed posture or creeping

朝向哪一个方向的眺望
这不可更改的姿势,或者爬行

Pursued for life in such deep universe
The pillar broken how many lies

环宇苍茫,生命有无追寻
这一柱擎天,刺破了多少谎言

16

Dusty land with way in and out
How many lives was grown in this space

大地混沌，来路去时又回
这一些虚空，孕育了丰盈

A myth called "Kwan–yin brought babies"

And another fact was question by the land

有一个神话叫观音送子
又一个现实被大地拷问

Utter sad calls of one´s
howling
Turnover of heaven and hell
in the cloud

仰天长啸者的一声悲鸣
云涛幻景里的天地翻覆

A ostrich back with stagger steps

No matter how long to wait but she never give up

有鸵鸟归来，或者缓步蹒跚
多么艰难一次等待，她没有放弃

Someone has seen the fairy
The palm he left

有人看见过那个仙风道骨人
他留下的这个手掌——

遥隔着的这些缝隙　　　To separate these lacune
使一对兄弟般眼神相似　　To make the expression in brother´s eyes similar

Have you seen such a huge peacock
Such a huge peacock display its beautiful tail feathers

有谁见过这样硕大的孔雀
这样硕大的孔雀开屏

Dear Mr. Lipo, you have been so many places

Hold wine in your hand and ask the heaven have you lost a friend

亲爱的李白先生,纵横四野
把酒问天,可曾少了一人

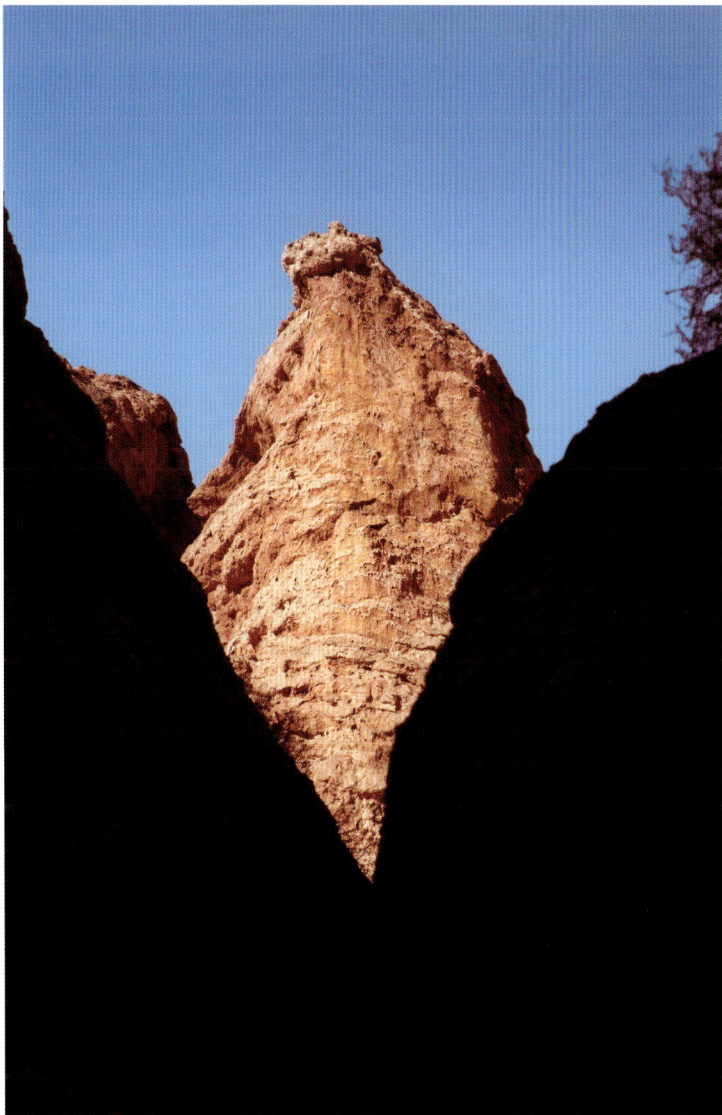

A gold bear dancing alone in the valley
These mountains fell back

一只金熊独舞山谷
那些纷纷让路的山峰向两边退去

多么像一双哺育中的鸟啊   Just like a fledgling
坚硬的利喙下，柔软的情怀   Soft heart under hard and sharp beak

This is a happy family   这是一个幸福的家庭
They walk on the top of mountain warm and moving   它们在山峰上行走,温暖而动人

This is await for thousands years

The WangFu mountain became a lonely mountain

这是一次千年的守望呀
望夫女壁立为一座孤独的山峰

A heart –shaped rock hang above the head

Some rock –shaped hard in soft

一块心一样的石头,悬在头顶
一些石头一样的心,在柔软中坚硬

The mysterious door of Tianshan mountains

When we have opened it and close but we don´t know

天山大峡谷的神秘城门
有哪一次被我们打开，又悄然关闭

Have you seen the stream
Rolling on the riverbed

你看见那一条飘垂而下的溪流
它干涸的河床上巨石滚动

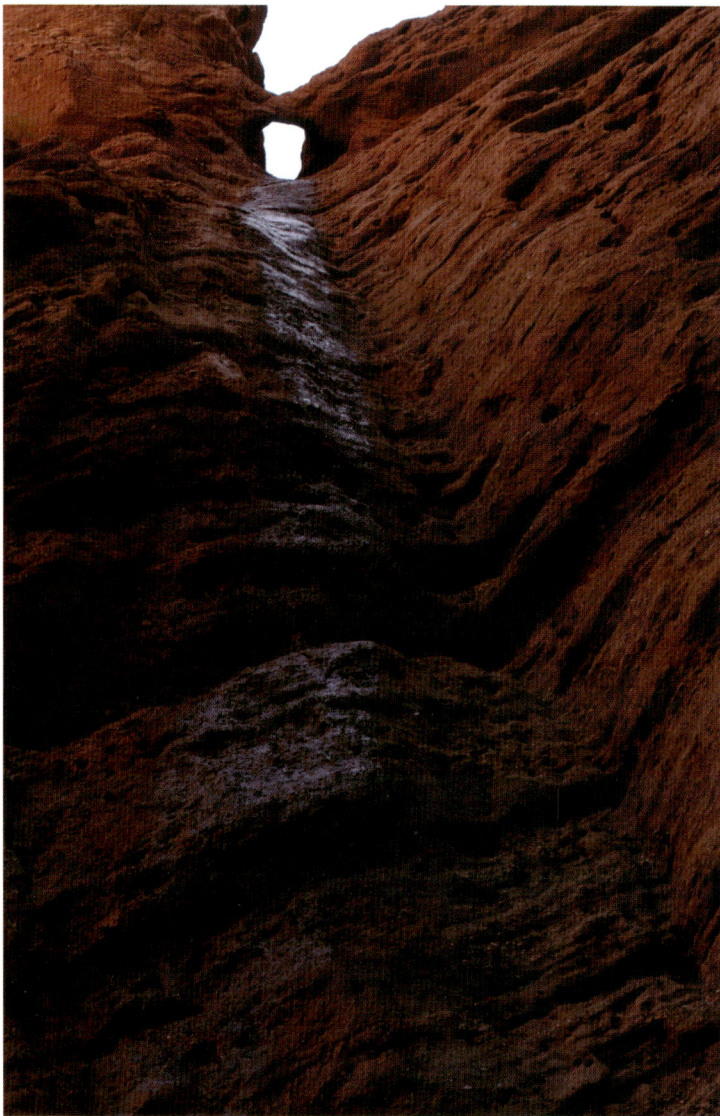

To built a way to heaven
And the bridge hang on our destiny

是要为自己打造一条天之路
那高悬在我们命运中的桥呀

Like sailboat racing

A moment in this thousands of mountains

犹如千帆竞渡

这万千山峰里的，一个瞬间

吉木乃县境内只有几条季节性内陆河流，主要分为两大水系：吉木乃内流水系包括乌拉斯特河、乌勒昆乌拉斯图河（即中哈界河）、塔斯特河等；布伦托海区内流水系包括哈尔交河、乌特布拉克河等。

如梦似幻的神石谷，是吉木乃县至今尚鲜为人知的一处大自然的杰作。由于各种原因，许多鬼斧神工般的奇异造型还有待更多的探险者去发现和命名。

and downfaulted basin. Kezileader, Mhabuqigai, Nuohai, Narenkala, Katu and more than 40 mountains in this area. On the west is Kumutuobie Desert , most of the dune is fixed type and half –fixed type which has elevation of 420m to 700m.

There´ s only some seasonal inland river in Jimnai. The two main river system is Jimnai internal River system which include Wulasite River and Wulekun-wulasitu River and Tasi River and Buluntuohai internal River system which include Haerjiao river and Butelake River.

The mysterious ShenshiValley is a masterpiece of nature which is undiscovered by peoples until nowadays. Because of many reasons, there are lots of mystery is expecting to be discovered and name.

We can not avoid the dispatch of god 　　　我们回避不了神的差遣
We are just some footprints on the grass land 　我们只是这草地上的,一行脚印

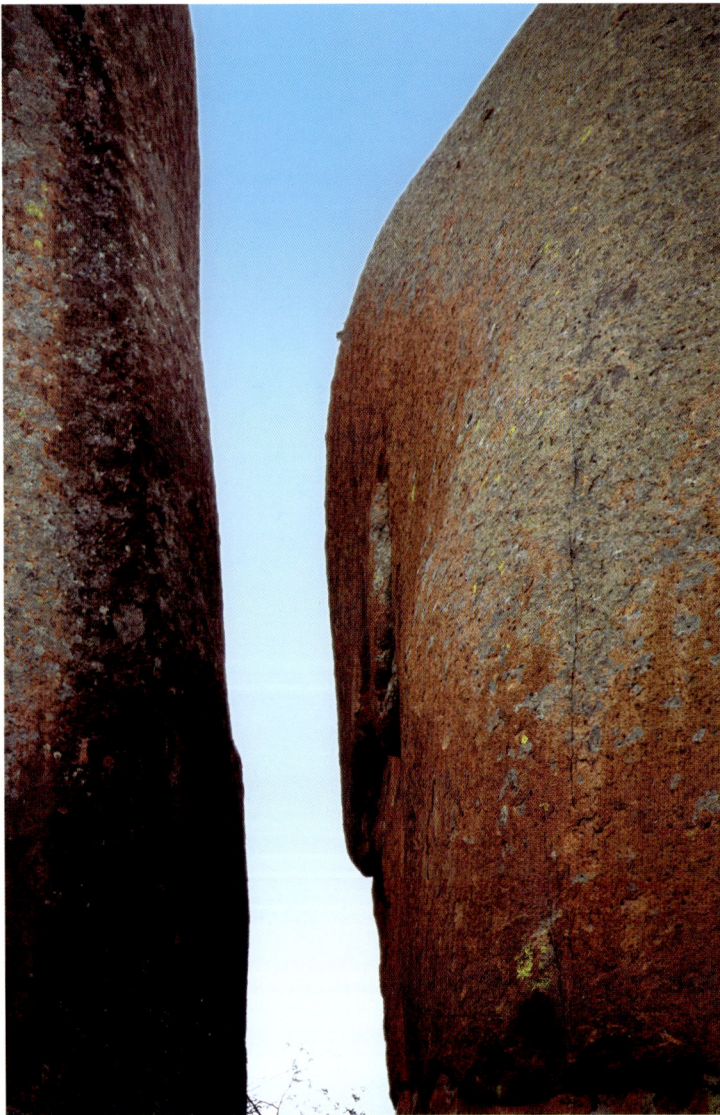

Yep , when the door of heaven opened
We can have our own happiness

是啊，只有这天门开启
我们才能够迎来自己的福祉

What kind of rocks they are
Grass full of land and the door opened

这是一些怎样的石头
青草铺地，而城门洞开

十里城墙，不变的柔肠
柔软的石头，固若金汤

10 miles city wall with non-changed gentle
Soft but impregnable

One man defense in grassland
But now we can not see any sign of war

有一夫当关,正是草色迷茫时
已看不见面目里的狰狞和远处的硝烟

This is armor of solider

These enemy runaway like the dust blow by strong wind

这是战士的盔甲,铁血的征衣
那些尘土飞扬,正在四季里逃散

42

Double-face life we never meet
Never abandon and holdout in the storm

这世间我们不曾一遇的双面人生
这风雨里的坚守和永不背弃

是邻家的一双好姊妹
她们丢弃了命运的面纱和青春的无悔

Neighbor´s sister
They abandon the veil of destiny and never regret of youth

A giant has cross time
And gaze at the past time faraway

有一个巨人他穿越了沧桑
凝眉远处,往事何其匆匆

只有这些自由的脸庞上镌刻着惬意　　　Only pleasing engrave on these free face
只有这些散落的石头,可以随意丢弃　　Only these fallout rocks can be throw anywhere

If there´ s two mail lion run together
There´ s no choice for the lean of world

如果只有"并驾齐驱"
这个世界的倾斜,似乎没有选择

What you can anaclitic is this green grass field

Up there is a firm shoulder

向下可以依附的,是这葱绿的草场

向上,有一双宽厚的肩膀

Mummy´s arm always
So firm and reliable

任何时间,母亲的怀抱
总是这样坚实而又可靠

这些鱼,这些石头一样的鱼呀　　These stone-like fishes
似乎早已经进入了漫长的睡眠　　Seems to be into a deep sleep

Hardening in the storm is in silent
And ancient time was pocking on rock

哪一些风雨里的锻打，正悄然进行
哪一些久远的时光，在石头上锈蚀

一次温暖的旅程,有足够的石头让我们
携带着这些光滑的记忆

A warm journey
There´s enough rocks for us to bring these sleek memories

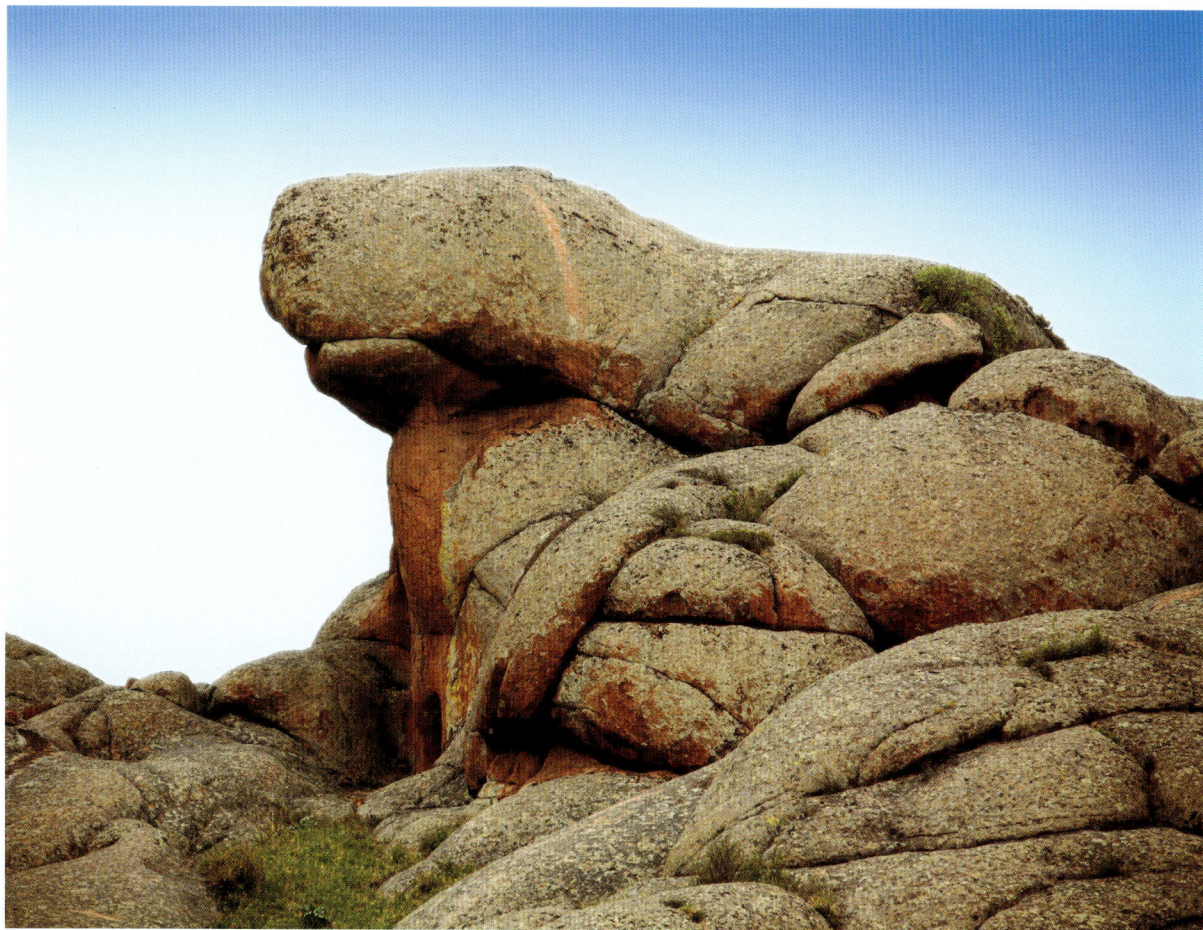

Frogs maybe forget their pool   青蛙们也忘记了曾经的水塘
Easy jump but no future   多么轻松的一跳，却是归途渺茫

有一些往事无法被诉说　　　　Something can not told
比如这些石头上石龟的记忆　　Like these stone tortoise on rocks

Otherwise why there´s fish head drown into the bottom of ocean
Such a inebriety suck

要不然,怎么会有鱼头沉入海底
多么陶醉的一次吮吸——

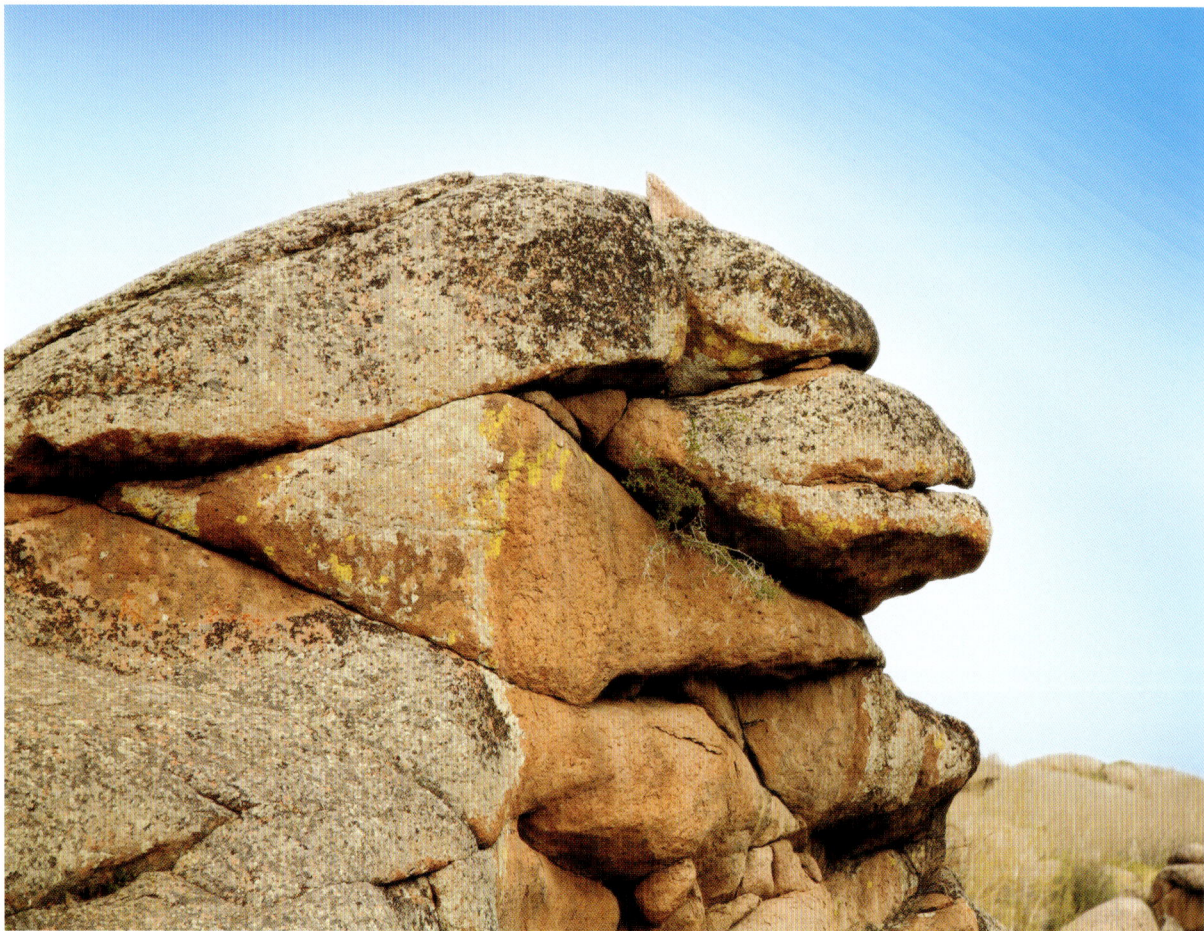

被这一只蝗虫啃食的草地上
土地正在露出斑驳的颜色

On this locust gnaw grassland
The field has expose its own color

What a dramatic sheep
Puppet expression full of shape of rock

多么喜剧的一只羊
木偶般的表情，全是石头的模样

我们快要遗忘了
留在后面的这一只小鸟,神色多么凄惶

We nearly forget
This little bird we left behind has such poor expression

The trees grown on the rock and stream flow through

Shake the world with their little body

生长在石头上的树，以及山泉
此刻用渺小的身影，晃动着一个世界

再也无法用遗忘来安慰你了　　　　Never can comfort you by forget
亲爱的老兄，你在这里等待了多久　How long have you been wait here dear buddy

Rock-shaped haystack and non-move barn
Some yellow flowers of homeland on this grassland

石头般的草垛,无法搬运的粮仓
此刻的草地上,几朵故乡里的黄花

多一些的明亮，开启心灵的这眼天窗
是我们穿越时空的仰望

We need more shining light to light up the window of heart
To look through the space

Some tiny crackle through the rock
And some dust we never clean them up

有细碎的裂纹从石头上穿过
有一些尘埃，我们已无力掸拂

多么久了,这荒废的城池
多么低矮的山石,正在越过我们内心的期望

We don´t the history of this obsolete city
No matter how the rock of mountain is now
through our expecting in our heart

THE DEVIL CITY OF GUQUNG

奇台魔鬼城

这是一个魔鬼的岗哨
不需要城堡的空旷的城门

This is a devil´s sentry
A lonely door without castle

THE DEVIL CITY OF GUQUNG

奇台魔鬼城

神秘莫测的奇台魔鬼城——将军戈壁深处隐藏着一座神秘莫测的古老城廓。这座城的面积大约80平方千米。每当夜间风起时，城内就会发出凄恻阴森的声音，听起来好像神话中魔鬼的叫声，所以人们称此地为魔鬼城。

魔鬼城内有许多惟妙惟肖的岩石造型，比如阿拉伯的清真寺、柬埔寨的吴哥窟、西藏的布达拉宫等等，有的还像农妇晚归、壮士观天、和尚念经、八戒睡觉、黄牛耕耘、熊猫打站、鲤鱼出水、猴子守山。这些似人似物的造型，全都栩栩如生。在地质学上，魔鬼城被称为风蚀地貌或雅丹地貌。这种地貌是由三叠系的各色沉积岩、侏罗系的各色沉积岩和白垩系的各色沉积岩组成，经过雨水的冲刷和风力的切割，天长日久就形成了这样绚丽多彩、姿态万千的自然景观。

由于风雨剥蚀，地面形成深浅不一的沟壑，裸露的石层被狂风雕琢得奇形怪状，在起伏的山坡上，布满血红、湛蓝、洁白、橙黄的各色石子，宛如魔女遗珠，更给其增添了几许神秘色

There is a mysterious ancient city deep in the General Gobi Desert which has area about 80 sq. km.

You can hear sad and terrified sound when the night fall and wind flowing, it sounds like cry of devil in the myth so people named here as The Devil City.

There are various shape of rock in this city, such as the Mosque of Arab, the Angkor wat of Cambodia and The Potala Palace of Tibet. Some like farmer going back home, warrior look at the sky, monk prayer, Bajie sleeping, bull plowing ad weeding, standing panda, swimming fish, monkey on the mountain. All of these are lifelike. It is called wind erosion land-form or yardangs.

This land feature is formed of colorful sedimentary rock of Triassic, Jurassic and Creatcic. Rain and wind for thousands of years, nature create a such wonderful scene.

Because of disintegration of rain and wind , the

彩,内城地处风口,四季多风。每当大风刮来,黄沙遮天,大风在风城里激荡回旋,凄厉呼啸,如同鬼哭,魔鬼城因此而得名。

魔鬼城属于雅丹地貌,在大自然鬼斧神工长期作用下,形成了一个梦幻般的迷宫世界,古今中外的名山胜迹应有尽有;各种各样的造景地貌琳琅满目,惟妙惟肖,置身于魔鬼城定能使你形象思维的特长得到充分发挥。

魔鬼城并非人力所为,它完全是大自然的手笔。不知多少年前,由于地壳的运动,这里形成了一些沙岩结构的山体,这些较为松软的岩石在千万年的剥蚀下,形成了千奇百怪的造型和大小小的洞穴。魔鬼城就是在这种外力作用下形成的。

阳光下的奇台魔鬼城,泛着红灿灿的光芒。土质因为风化表面变成了硬壳,这种地貌和风化了的巨石,给人一种很远古的感觉。

shape of land-surface and rocks was carved and has many strange shape. Colorful carpolite everywhere on the hillside, they looks like lost pearl of witch. The inner city is on the place where is windy all over the year. When wind was blowing, the sky was covered by sand and wind running in the city making sound like monster crying and that´s why people named here The Devil City.

Yardangs of the devil city was formed a fantasy world which has all the famous scene spot of china and foreign country. If you are in it , you will find that you can get more imagination.

You don´t know how many years earlier the nature built this mysterious city, the move of the Earth´s crust, some sandstone mountains were formed and these soft rock was blow by rain and wind to from this devil city.

The devil city of Guqung City under the sunshine will bring you back to the ancient time and these huge rocks can shock you from your heart.

这是一个魔鬼的岗哨
不需要城堡的空旷的城门

This is a devil´s sentry
A lonely door without castle

How slowly you need to move
To shake the next slumber of this world

你需要有多么缓慢的移动
来撼动这个世界的下一次睡眠

It´s the face of antic
Most of the times we turn a blind eye

这个小丑的面目荒诞不经
在更多的时候，我们视而不见

We all make ourselves so poor
But the flower of fact bloom in our heart

我们都曾经让自己变得如此不堪
而真实的花朵在内心里开放

这绝对不是一个世纪的决战　　This is not an all decisive battle
哪怕荒原上只留下孤单的怀念　Even there´s only memories of loneliness left on the wasteland

The drop of water that we have waiting for long enough

已经足够久了
伸长了脖子也盼不下来的，那一滴水

But the wind used to be scraped out these ruined cotton

A bird´s nest on such a huge head

但是风，曾经掏空了这些破败的棉絮

硕大的头顶上，是一只鸟的居所

The large post of dinosaur century

With the last desolate painted by the setting sun

恐龙时代的巨幅宣传画
夕阳涂满了最后的荒凉

Turn back at this wasteland
The steps flit like dust

调过头来, 这片焦赫的土地
尘土一样掠过的脚步啊

76

The last dinner
Shadows of ruin everywhere

一场最后的欢宴
残迹里的阴霾无处不在

世界只剩下了这一副模样　　　　Some posture we never choose
有一些姿势是我们无法选择的　　Because the world make us to be

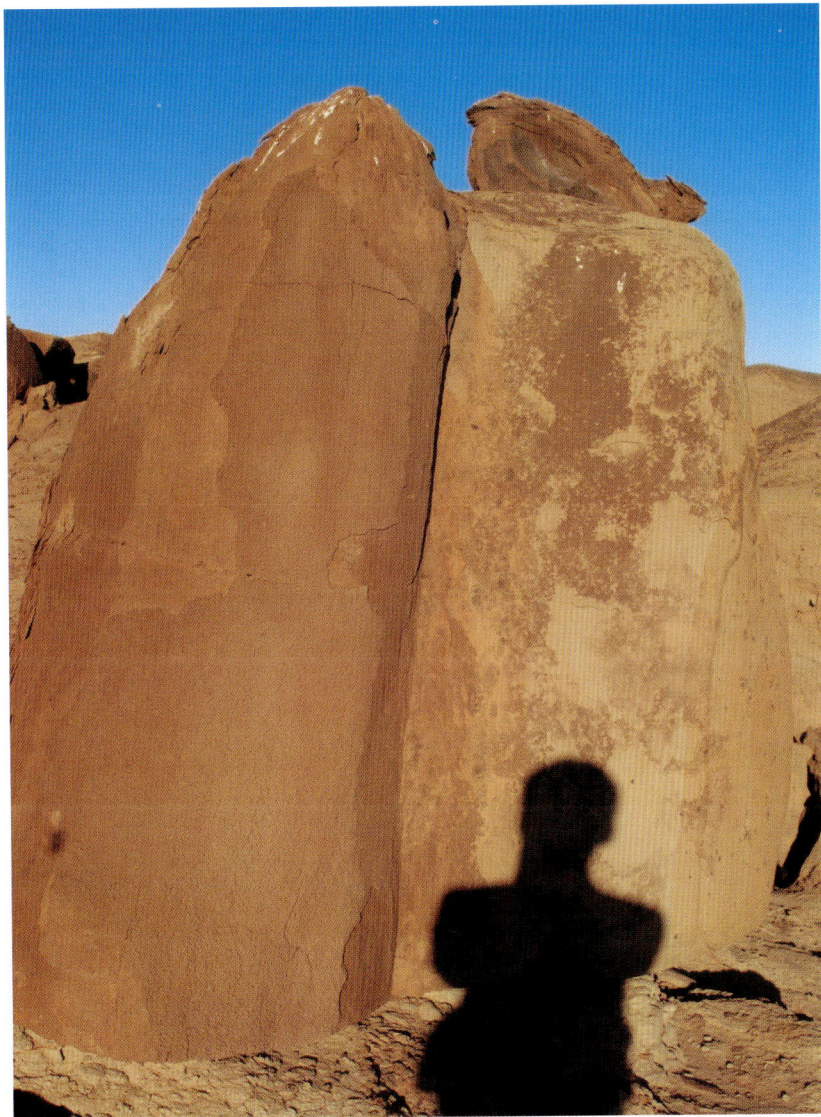

A bird left on the highland
Whether it has forgot of fly
or furl its wings

遗落在高处的一只鸟
它忘记了飞翔还是收拢了翅膀

Eyes sharp as knife
But can not avoid the destiny to be cut down

有着刀一样锋利的眼睛
却无法逃避被斩断的命运

Actually we can not handle our situation
On the top of the world

其实在世界的高处
我们并不能准确地把握自身的处境

遥相呼应着,那些坍塌的年代
在没有彻底地断裂之前,我们相互取暖

We shout and take warm form each other
Before the land was full break down

Make a great wall with our body
And make a mountain with our steel spirits

用我们的身躯筑就一条长城
此起彼伏的, 是我们钢铁般的意志

向最后的战场告别
还是向不妥协的命运，挥一挥手

Shake your hands
To the last battleground or to the uncompromising destiny

The large nest catch the wing of the wind
When it was falling down

就要倾斜了,这巨大的鸟巢
它最后抓住了风的翅膀

是荒原在我们的身后退却
苍凉的美景，如梦似幻

The beautiful scene as dream and imagine
Is the wasteland falling back behind us

Don´t ask anything of the ancient times
Just look at this huge and firm castle

看这恢宏的气势, 坚固的城堡
不要问我们岁月里的沧桑

THE COLORFUL CITY

五彩城

五彩城位于古尔班通古特沙漠东部的吉木萨尔县境内，县城以北 150 千米。它西临沙漠，东近黑色将军戈壁，东南 30 多千米是奇台魔鬼城，北靠卡拉麦里山。

走进五彩城，就像走进梦幻世界，光怪陆离的色彩从四面八方向你涌来，那么突兀，那么强烈，那么丰富多彩，那么变化无常，令人目眩。举目展望，那些大大小小五颜六色的山冈，错落有致地峥嵘着、斑驳着，呈现出千姿百态、扑朔迷离的景观。任何画家，都难以画出如此波澜壮阔、出神入化的不朽画卷。

五彩城的晚霞更是迷人。落日在告别大漠的那一刻把五彩城点燃，所有的山丘都像戴上了面具，红的如火，黄的如金，绿的可爱，蓝的诱人。登上山丘回望，那更是目不暇接。高底不等的山丘如哈萨克帐房，当然是彩色帐房，顶子是黄的，下边有灰色，有青色，有黛色，有黑黄，有橙色，有褐色，有红色，一层一层，既分明又相

Colorful City located in the Gurbantunggut Desert in the eastern part of Jimsar County, 150 km north of the town. Desert on its west and Gobi General on the east, about 30 kilometers on the southeast of Guqung is the odd Devil City, Karameh on the north.

Into the colorful city, just like into the dream land, the bizarre color coming to you from all directions, so unexpected, strong, rich, volatile, dizzying. Outlook, you might see, those colorful, large and small hill like the steps of land and colorful paint, a mottled showing thousands and confusing landscape. Any artist, it is difficult to draw such a magnificent, impressive immortal picture.

The sunset of Colorful City is more charming. Sunset lighting the Colorful City at the moment farewell the desert, all the hills are like wearing a mask, fiery red, yellow such as gold, the lovely green and blue attractive. Looking back on the hill, it is

间,既明丽又柔和。晚霞下的山丘都在竭力展示着各种姿容,或龙或蟒,或狮或豹,或塔或峰,或楼或亭,或伞或廊,真个是千姿百态,奇形怪状,扑朔迷离。

dizzying. At the end of the range of high hills such as Kazak accountant, of course, colorful accountant, the top is yellow, gray below, blue, dark green, yellow, black, orange, brown, red, both clear and white, both soft ,clear and beautiful. Hills under the sunglow are displaying variety of posture, dragon or python, leopard or lion, tower or peak, floor or kiosk, umbrella or gallery. The scenes here are varied types and poses, different shapes, strange and confusing.

The blood in these color, the frozen tears
How many color pens can write them down

这些色彩里的血,和凝固的泪
用多少枝彩笔记下的,风霜和记忆

那些红在金粉里渗出
那些磅礴、弯曲和畅达的五彩城谷

The huge colorful city
With red in gold

Falling or another cirfling
The hill firm shape like a straw hat

是坠落，或者是又一次盘旋
这个草帽一样的坚实的山丘

一座又一座红色的山寨
它们曾经在水中驻扎，又将注定被大水遗弃

Sand underwater and
These water looks like come from the sky

Even we can not see the real face of hero
But we can find them on these colored sand hills

这些红丝线扯动着水一样的天际
这些流水下面的，一层层细壤

即使这一刻我们窥不见英雄的面目
这些被色彩涂抹的沙丘上, 已依稀可见

Through this mountain there
Where is our real color

Freedom used to be run
through our shoulder
But there used to be ocean

翻过这一道山梁，在万千沟壑间
哪一处低洼里，才是我们真实的颜色

97

这是一片片水的海疆　　　　These red mountain village used to stand in water
自由曾经与我们擦肩而过　　And destine given up by the ocean

The running water will take the last color   那些浩荡的水呀
To which direction and falling back   带着这最后的色彩向哪一方向, 退却

如果一座山峦就是一束花朵　　　　If one mountain is a flower
那么这些连片的山峦应在哪里开放　　Then where should this chain of mountains bloom

String more mountains together with colorful silk thread
Head for the direction of those river falling back

用五色的丝线串起更多的山冈
沿着那些大水退却的方向——

这是一个真实的背影　　　This is a real figure viewed from behind
手挽着手，兄弟般的臂膀　Hand in hand, like brother

Who opened up this corridor of color
The silence like home

是谁为我们开辟了这段彩色的走廊
空阔处的寂静,一如故乡

这非凡的塔,真实的幻影　　　The real mirage of remarkable tower
撑破了视野里的,高天和流云　　Has crushed the cloud and sky in our view

You don´t know where to rely on
And where to can be depend on

那些依附也完全不知所措
高地上的攀援，已无迹可寻

Snow of somewhere and salt in the red mud

Pain was expended slowly in this season

哪里的雪,红壤里的盐
疼痛在这个季节里,一点点扩展

I was reminded the flam in winter   在我们推开这些山峦之前

Before we pull these mountains away   我曾想起，那些冬天里的火焰

这是我们命运的山崖　　　　This is the cliff of our destiny
也是我们不得不分别的,回乡的高台　　And it´s also the high platform we have to depart

THE FAIRY VALLEY OF KUTUBI

呼图壁神仙谷

这里是野生动物的乐园，更是冒险家的天堂。徒步在呼图壁大峡谷的心脏地带，耳边是咆哮的呼图壁河水，眼前是一个接一个的达坂，大峡谷不仅仅是在考验你的气力，更多的是在锤炼你的心志。走在群狼守护的地方，需要非凡的勇气，这勇气将指引你前往精神之国的极度空间！

呼图壁大河谷不同于一般的天山河谷，它发源于天山东段海拔 5290 米的河源峰，河谷纵深 40 余千米。河谷两侧高山耸立，森林浓蔽，花草奇异，遮天蔽日。谷底则地势险要，道路崎岖。由于河谷地处天山北坡，每到夏季，丰富的雨水和发源于河源峰周围众多雪山的融水，在谷底交汇成河，顺陡峭狭窄的峡谷咆哮而下，震耳欲聋。当你站在海拔 3862 米的前后山的分水岭——白杨沟达坂上，举目南望，形如尖塔的河源峰主峰时而云雾弥漫，若隐若现；时而天高云淡，冰山毕现。在哈萨克语中，河源峰被称为狼塔，意即"有群狼守护的塔山"。由于进山线路极其艰难漫长，当地牧民也很少

This is the eden of wild animals and the heaven of explorers. When you are walking in the heart-zone of The Great Canyon Of Kutubi , hearing the howling of the river and looking at the changeable views. It´s not only testing your body but also testing your spirit. You need marvelous courage to walk here and this courage will lead you to the country of spirit.

The Great Stream valley Of Kutubi is not same as general stream valley of Tianshan Mountains. It origin from the Heyuan peak which is on the east wing of Tianshan Mountains has the elevation of 5290m, the depth of the valley is about 40km. High mountain, forest, singularity flower and grass covered the sky, the topography of the bottom is very dangerous and the way here is difficult to walk on it. Because the valley is located on the north slope of Tianshan Mountains there is enough rain and the melting snow water from the Heyuan peak get together and formed a large river on the bottom of the valley. When you are standing on the poplar valley mountain which has the elevation of 3862, you will see the main peak of Heyuan in the cloud. The Heyuan peak is called "the tower of wolves" in Kazak language which means "the tower mountain which guarded by wolves". Because the route of getting into the mountain, the

接近。在后山纵深 120 千米的无人区里，冰山隘口令人生畏。

呼图壁县历史悠久，文化繁荣，早在西周时期，呼图壁人的祖先就在这里繁衍生息，耕耘劳作。他们创造了灿烂的文化，写下了光辉的历史。

康家石门子岩雕刻画康家石门子画位于昌吉州呼图壁县的天山腹地，两条山溪汇流处的西北岸的岩石岩面平整，岩刻面约 220 平方米，雕刻着 300 余人，大者高 2.04 米，小者 19 厘米。有男有女，或站或卧，或衣或裸，男女合图、双头同体、三头同体图像，真实地体现了原始人祈求生育、繁衍人口的群婚制生活场面。这处岩画经有关专家论证定为距今近 3000 年前的塞人所为。

距今 2500 多年前，塞人就已活动在帕米尔、天山及北疆大部分地区。同众多的游牧民族一样，他们的经济生活以随畜逐水草为主，且兼营冶炼、加工铁器。公元前 3 世纪末进入阶级社会，建立国家政权，最高统治者称塞王。塞人喜欢戴尖顶帽，崇尚各种饰牌金饰片、铜器及各种野兽纹图案。古代塞人入居西域后，曾在新疆历史舞台上扮演过举足轻重的角色。

local people is rarely get close to it. When you are in the no man´s land , the mouth of the icy mountain will make you fear.

Kutubi has long history and prosperous culture. The people of Kutubi were live here and harvest long time ago about The Westliche Zhou-Dynasty. The built gorgeous culture and write down their history.

The paint of Kangjiashimenzi is located deep in the Tianshan Mountain of Kutubi in Changji prefecture. It has area about 220 sq. m. and more than 300 peoples on the drawing. The height of big one is about 2.04m and the smaller one is about 19cm. The drawing is about the ancient people´s daily life such as clothing , sex. Some of the people on the paint is wearing cloth but some of them have no cloth on their body, some of them are standing and some of them are lying. Experts says that people on the drawing is Sai who is living at 3000years ago.

About 2500years ago, Sais were living at the highland of Pamir and Tianshan Mountains and most area of northern Xinjiang. They graze with grassland like most of the nomad. But they also making iron tools. They entered class society 3 BC and the emperor they called "The king of Sais"

Sais like wearing peaked cap, they like all kinds of silk and gold pieces of jewelry bronze container and picture of wild animals. The ancient Sais play an important role in the history of Xinjiang after the moved into the Westfield.

比如我们打开了一道缓慢的山谷
艰难的草和视野里的苍茫

As we open a slowly valley
We can see nothing in our vision

You can feel nothing
Even wind in The Fairy
Valley

神仙谷呀，飘然不觉中
哪怕你脚下的一阵微风，
都不曾翻动

Cold to which direction
And where the grass lead us to

朝向哪一个高处的寒冷
草色里的迷茫,蜿蜒而去

That is the home of angels   那才是神仙们的居所

Wind knock at door gently   哪些风，轻轻叩打的门环

这是神仙的后花园　　　　　This is angel´s back garden

清凉的草地上阳光照亮了城堡　　The sun lighting the castle on the cold clear grassland

Maybe we have forgotten other growing
And these bare freedom and expecting

或许我们忘记了另一些生长
那些根须裸露的自由和向往

曾经有过被斩断的历史　　　　　Used to be cut down
多么缓慢的等待,不仅仅只是生长　But no matter how slow they are growing

The lonely flower blooming
Although four season has gone

盛开在绿野中的,孤单的花朵
四季消亡了,你依然怒放

康家石门子的岩壁上
古老的生命比真实更有力量

The ancient life is more powerful
On the crag of Kangjiashimengzi

Look, which palace can be more spectacular
And where has angels there

看呀，有哪一处的宫殿如此壮观
哪一处的高台上，神一般的居所

向着两边打开一道又一道山门　　　The door of heaven one by one

无处逃遁的地老天荒　　　　　　　Time can escape nowhere

The corridor built in the sky
And grass was waving in the song of bird

这些建设在高空中的走廊
此刻的青草在鸟声里摇曳

我们无法掀动这些巨石的耸立
这些空中的花园里四季分明

We can not move these huge rocks
Four season were so clear in these garden

This is city faraway

This is another garden in the valley

这是远处的城市

这是山谷里的，另一处花园

这些遮阳伞无法撑开的
是山峦后面的美景和眺望

Beach umbrella can not show us
The beauty scene behind mountains